Lisa Hudson

☑ **W9-DHK-173**

Weekly Reader Children's Book Club presents

WHAT CAN YOU MAKE OF IT?

by
FRANZ BRANDENBERG

illustrated by
ALIKI

Greenwillow
Read-alone

GREENWILLOW BOOKS

A Division of William Morrow & Company, Inc. | New York

The art was prepared in pen and ink, with crayon overlays for the yellow, red, and black.

Library of Congress Cataloging in Publication Data
Brandenberg, Franz. What can you make of it? (Greenwillow read-alone series)
Summary: A family of field mice finally find a way to use their collection of rubbish.
[1. Mice—Fiction. 2. Recycling (Waste)—Fiction. 3. Handicraft—Fiction]
I. Aliki. II. Title. PZ7.B7364Wh [E] 76-44406
ISBN 0-688-80083-1 ISBN 0-688-84083-3 lib. bdg.

Weekly Reader Children's Book Club Edition

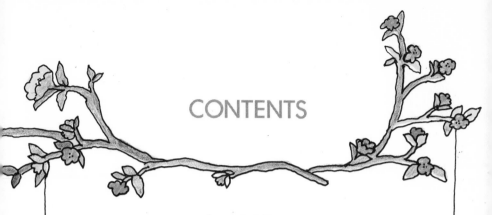

CONTENTS

CHAPTER 1

PACKING

Mr. and Mrs. Fieldmouse
and their six children
were moving.

"This is a good time
   to get rid of your rubbish,"
   said Father Fieldmouse.
"We don't have any rubbish,"
   the children replied.
"What about the orange juice cans?"
   asked Father Fieldmouse.

"We'd like to keep them, please!"
replied Annette.
"If you don't get rid
   of the orange juice cans, we'll need
   not one but two moving vans,"
   said Father Fieldmouse.
"We'll find some use
   for them some day,"
   said Mother Fieldmouse.

"What about the milk cartons?"
asked Father Fieldmouse.
"We'd like to keep them, please!"
replied Bertrand.

10

"If you don't get rid

of the milk cartons, we'll need

not two but three moving vans,"

said Father Fieldmouse.

"We'll find some use

for them some day,"

said Mother Fieldmouse.

"What about the toilet paper tubes?"

asked Father Fieldmouse.

"We'd like to keep them, please!"

replied Colette.

"If you don't get rid
of the toilet paper tubes, we'll need
not three but four moving vans,"
said Father Fieldmouse.

"We'll find some use
for them some day,"
said Mother Fieldmouse.

"What about the yarn spools?"
asked Father Fieldmouse.
"We'd like to keep them, please!"

replied Daniel.

"If you don't get rid

of the yarn spools, we'll need

not four but five moving vans,"

said Father Fieldmouse.

"We'll find some use

for them some day,"

said Mother Fieldmouse.

"What about the egg cartons?"
asked Father Fieldmouse.

"We'd like to keep them, please!"
replied Esther.

"If you don't get rid
of the egg cartons, we'll need
not five but six moving vans,"
said Father Fieldmouse.

"We'll find some use

for them some day,"

said Mother Fieldmouse.

"What about the old magazines?"

asked Father Fieldmouse.

"We'd like to keep them, please!"

replied Ferdinand.

"If you don't get rid

    of the old magazines, we'll need

    not six but seven moving vans,"

    said Father Fieldmouse.

"We'll find some use

    for them some day,"

    said Mother Fieldmouse.

Mr. and Mrs. Fieldmouse

and their six children

packed all their rubbish.

They needed not one, not two,

not three, not four, not five,

not six, but seven moving vans.

CHAPTER 2

UNPACKING

Mr. and Mrs. Fieldmouse's
new house
was an old house.
"Where can we put
the orange juice cans?"
asked Annette.

"Not in the living room, please!"
replied Mother Fieldmouse.

"We'll find some place for them,"
said Father Fieldmouse.

"Where can we put the milk cartons?"
asked Bertrand.

"Not in the dining room, please!"
replied Mother Fieldmouse.

"We'll find some place for them,"

said Father Fieldmouse.

"Where can we put

the toilet paper tubes?"

asked Colette.

"Not in the kitchen, please!"

replied Mother Fieldmouse.

"We'll find some place for them,"

said Father Fieldmouse.

"Where can we put the yarn spools?"
asked Daniel.

"Not in the library, please!"
replied Mother Fieldmouse.

"We'll find some place for them,"
said Father Fieldmouse.

"Where can we put
the egg cartons?"
asked Esther.

"Not in the bathroom, please!"
replied Mother Fieldmouse.

"We'll find some place for them,"
said Father Fieldmouse.

"Where can we put the old magazines?"
asked Ferdinand.

"Not in the bedrooms, please!"
replied Mother Fieldmouse.

"We'll find some place for them,"
said Father Fieldmouse.

"Where will we put

all the rubbish?"

asked Mother Fieldmouse.

"In the garage,"

replied Father Fieldmouse.

"Garages are for cars,"

said Mother Fieldmouse.

"But we don't have a car,"

said Father Fieldmouse.

"Then let's put the rubbish

in the garage,"

said Mother Fieldmouse.

Mr. and Mrs. Fieldmouse

and their six children

unpacked the orange juice cans,

the milk cartons,

the toilet paper tubes,

the yarn spools, the egg cartons,

and the old magazines.

They put them in the garage.

CHAPTER 3

VISITORS

"Uncle Alfred and Aunt Kate
are coming to visit us,"
said Father Fieldmouse.
"How nice!" shouted the children.
"We'll have to clean out the garage,"
said Mother Fieldmouse.
"Why?" asked Father Fieldmouse.

"To make room for their car,"

replied Mother Fieldmouse.

"There is plenty of room

in front of the house,"

said Father Fieldmouse.

"That would be wasting the garage,"

said Mother Fieldmouse.

"Garages are for cars."

Mr. and Mrs. Fieldmouse

and their six children

cleaned out the garage.

They put the orange juice cans

in the dining room,

the milk cartons in the living room,

the toilet paper tubes in the library,

the yarn spools in the kitchen,

the egg cartons in the bedrooms, and

the old magazines in the bathroom.

There was now plenty of room

in the garage for the car.

"A nice new old house
   you have here,"
   said Uncle Alfred.
"But there is not much room
   to get around," said Aunt Kate.
"And there is no place at all
   to sit down."

"It's because of all the rubbish,"

said Father Fieldmouse.

"What rubbish?" asked Uncle Alfred.

"The orange juice cans,

the milk cartons,

the toilet paper tubes,

the yarn spools,

the egg cartons,

and the old magazines,"

replied Mother Fieldmouse.

"You'll find some use for them

some day," said Aunt Kate.

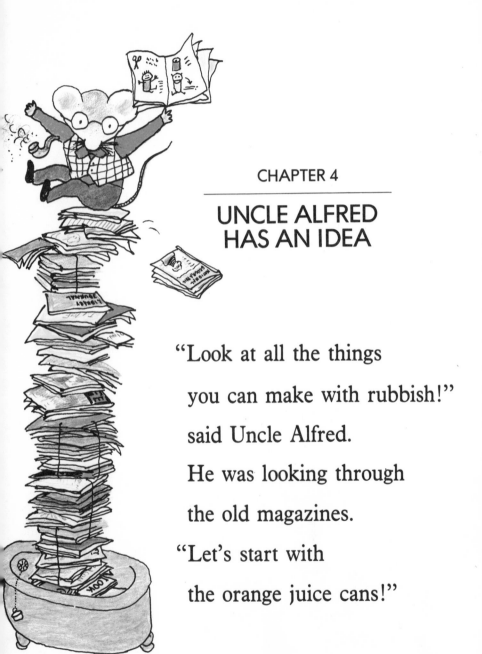

CHAPTER 4

UNCLE ALFRED HAS AN IDEA

"Look at all the things
you can make with rubbish!"
said Uncle Alfred.
He was looking through
the old magazines.
"Let's start with
the orange juice cans!"

They all went into the dining room
and made things with
the orange juice cans.
Mother Fieldmouse made lions.
Father Fieldmouse made tigers. ·
The children made horses.
Aunt Kate made bears.
And Uncle Alfred made a top hat.

When they had used up
all the orange juice cans,
Uncle Alfred said,
"Look at all the things you can make
with yarn spools!"
They all went into the kitchen and
made things with the yarn spools.
Mother Fieldmouse made snakes.
Father Fieldmouse made a trapeze.
The children made monkeys.
Aunt Kate made a clown.
And Uncle Alfred made a rattle.

36

When they had used up
all the yarn spools,
Uncle Alfred said,
"Look at all the things you can
make with toilet paper tubes!"
They all went into the library
and made things with
the toilet paper tubes.

What's the matter
with Bertrand?

BOO!

Mother Fieldmouse made

a whole family of elephants.

Father Fieldmouse made a microphone.

The children made opera glasses.

Aunt Kate made a hoop.

And Uncle Alfred made a cannon.

When they had used up
all the toilet paper tubes,
Uncle Alfred said,
"Look at all the things you can
make with egg cartons!"
They all went into the bedrooms
and made things with the egg cartons.
Mother Fieldmouse made turtles.

Father Fieldmouse made pedestals.
The children made cups.

Aunt Kate made owls.

And Uncle Alfred made a rabbit.

When they had used up
all the egg cartons,
Uncle Alfred said,
"Look at all the things you
can make with milk cartons!"

They all went into the living room
and made cages for the animals
with the milk cartons.
"We have made a whole circus!"
said Uncle Alfred.

In you go.

"I am glad we saved all the rubbish!"
said Father Fieldmouse.
"I always said we'd have
some use for it some day,"
said Mother Fieldmouse.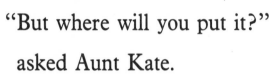
"But where will you put it?"
asked Aunt Kate.
"In the garage," said Uncle Alfred.

"Garages are for cars,"
said Mother Fieldmouse.
"There is plenty of room for
the car in front of the house,"
said Uncle Alfred.
He went to park his car
in front of the house.

They put the animals in the cages
and carried the whole circus
into the garage.

"What about the old magazines?"
asked Mother Fieldmouse.

"Let's put them in the library,"
said Father Fieldmouse.

"You might have some use for them
some day again," said Uncle Alfred.

"We now have room to get around,"
said Mother Fieldmouse.

"And there is plenty of room to sit."
Aunt Kate went to read
in the library.

Uncle Alfred settled
in the living room.

Mother and Father Fieldmouse
went into the kitchen
to cook dinner.

The children set the table

in the dining room.

"Dinner is served!"

called Mother Fieldmouse.

They all took turns in the bathroom.

Then they gathered

in the dining room

for a big Sunday dinner.

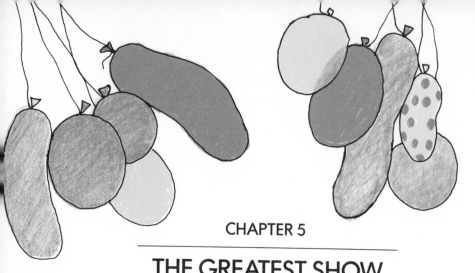

CHAPTER 5

THE GREATEST SHOW
ON EARTH

After dinner they all went

down to the garage.

Mother Fieldmouse gave everyone

a cupful of popcorn.

Father Fieldmouse handed out

the opera glasses.

wait for me!

Uncle Alfred shook the rattle.

"Ladies and gentlemen!" he said

into the microphone.

"The greatest show on earth

is about to begin."

Father Fieldmouse made

the monkeys fly on the trapeze.

Annette made the lions

sit on the pedestals.

Bertrand made the tigers

jump through the hoop.

Mother Fieldmouse
made the elephants
make a pyramid.
Colette made
the bears dance.

ha

Aunt Kate made the clown

pull the rabbit out of the top hat.

Daniel made the horses trot

around the ring.

Esther made the owls ride

on the turtles.

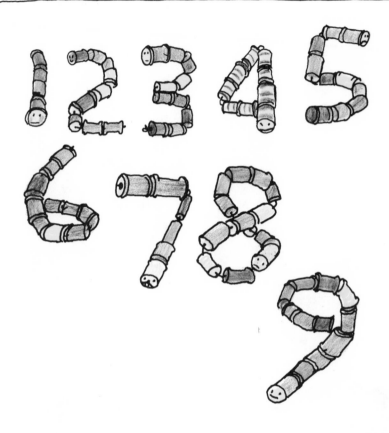

Ferdinand made the snakes

write the numbers one to nine.

54

And for the climax, Uncle Alfred
shot the clown out of the cannon.
They all applauded each other.
"That was fun!" they said.

"Oh dear, I'm afraid it is time
for us to leave," said Aunt Kate.
"Already?" asked the children.
"They'll come again soon,"
said Father Fieldmouse.

Uncle Alfred and Aunt Kate

climbed into their car

and drove away.

Mother and Father Fieldmouse,

their six children,

and the whole circus

waved to them

until they were out of sight.